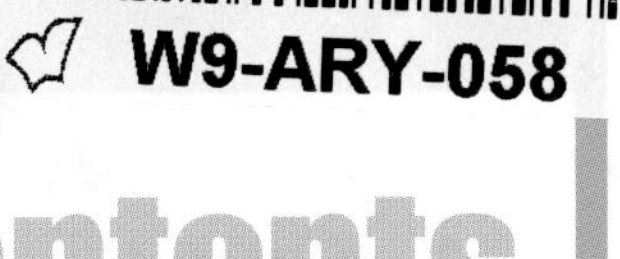

Contents

Special Features

2 Reefs of the World

Reefs are part of an incredible underwater world. Explore some of these amazing natural structures.

12 Mystery of the Coral Reef

A traumatic shipwreck experience leaves Jack unable to remember his past. Will it ever come back to him?

22 Treasure

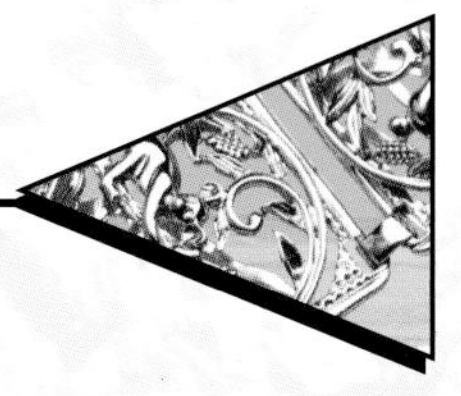

Playing on the beach after a storm, Nathan, Emerald, and Amos make an exciting discovery.

Features

Safari POWER

Test your word knowledge 10

How much of an expert were you? 21

Poetry Corner

Breakfast 11

Coral Canyons 30

Safari Point of View

What do you think? 20

readingsafari.com

Check out what's on the Safari web site 32

Reefs of the World

Written by James Laurie

Reefs are places of wonder to visit, explore, and read about. Many of these fascinating natural structures are scattered throughout the Pacific Ocean, although reefs are also found in the Indian Ocean and in other areas. Some of these reefs are known for their unique and striking beauty, others for their diversity of marine life, some for their size, or for all of these elements.

For whatever reason, each year a huge number of divers explore the beautiful underwater world of reefs. However, some people believe that it would be better if the reefs were left alone, so that the coral and other marine life could thrive without threat of damage or destruction. Many reefs around the world are currently under threat from overfishing and pollution, among other things.

Reefs offer a wonderful underwater world for divers to explore.

Great Barrier Reef

The Great Barrier Reef of Australia is one of the world's natural wonders. It is the largest coral reef in the world. Created over millions of years by marine creatures called polyps, whose limestone skeletal structures form the reef, it extends over 1,249 miles (2,010 km). It runs along the northeastern coast of Australia. Starting just south of the Tropic of Capricorn, it follows the Australian coastline to end in the Torres Strait, just south of Papua New Guinea.

Covering an area of 135,145 square miles (350,000 sq km), the reef is approximately half the size of the state of Texas, or the size of Scotland and England combined.

More than 2,500 reefs make up the giant reef we call the Great Barrier. People say it is the biggest structure ever built by living creatures. In fact, the reef is so big that it can be seen from space. The first time the reef was fully mapped was in 1968 when it was photographed from the spacecraft *Apollo 7* as it circled the Earth.

Great Barrier Reef is the largest coral reef in the world and home to a multitude of marine species.

The Great Barrier Reef has several major threats to its continued existence. Firstly, the pollution created by humans and the damage inflicted by divers, often unintentionally, is causing the coral creatures to die.

As well as this, the reef is being attacked by hordes of crown-of-thorns starfish, which feed on marine polyps. These starfish have destroyed many of the coral colonies in the southwest Pacific Ocean. There has been an increase in numbers of the starfish for which scientists have, as yet, been unable to find a reason.

Finally, silica sands on the beaches and limestone particles from the floor of the reef are valuable for agriculture. It is also thought that there may be oil beneath the reef. Petroleum companies want permission to drill for this.

If the reef's sands and beaches are dredged and if oil is drilled for beneath the reef, a creation of nature that took millions of years to develop could die in just a few years.

Drilling for oil could prove disastrous for the Great Barrier Reef.

The Coral Sea

Beyond the Great Barrier Reef lies the Coral Sea. Just below the surface in parts of this vast sea is a world of reefs. Huge stretches of atoll reefs lurk beneath the crystal-clear ocean water and offer divers many irresistible opportunities.

The coral colonies of the Coral Sea are huge. At 138 feet (42 m) below the ocean's surface, there are colonies of soft coral, 8 feet (2.5 m) high, swaying with the movement of the sea. Here among the reef dwellers, deadly stonefish, massive groupers, moray eels, and manta rays glide by. Huge whale sharks slip silently past.

Huge stretches of atoll reefs lurk beneath the crystal-clear ocean water and offer divers many irresistible opportunities.

Diving in the Coral Sea

Osprey Reef

Situated in the Coral Sea, Osprey Reef rises vertically from a depth of 1000 feet (305 m) to the ocean's surface. It is what is known as an oceanic seamount, or underwater mountain. On the sheer face of the reef coral grows.

North Horn, at the very end of Osprey Reef, 80 miles (129 km) northeast of Lizard Island, has northbound currents on both sides. The meeting of these currents creates deep turbulent waters that attract a huge variety of plankton, fish, and particularly sharks. At 69–88.5 feet (21–27 m) deep, a coral ledge forms a feeding place for sharks. With as many as 20 sharks patrolling at any given time, as well as voracious moray eels, hungry schools of barracuda, manta rays, tuna, grouper, and even whale sharks, North Horn is the perfect place to observe a huge variety of sea life.

Marion Reef

Action Point at Marion Reef, also located in the Coral Sea, is another popular feeding spot for sharks. At the tip of the reef the waters are home to a multitude of different species of marine life, many of which are food for sharks.

In the lagoon at Marion Reef are about 50 other reefs. From a depth of 180–200 feet (55–61 m), the coral spires soar near the surface of the water. Angelfish glide among colonies of yellow coral. The clear water makes it a good place for photographers.

Across the Coral Sea heading east lie the islands of Fiji. These islands with their reefs attract divers from all over the world.

Angelfish glide among colonies of yellow coral. The clear water makes it a wonderful place for photographers.

Fiji

Beqa, Astrolabe Reef, Rainbow Reef, Moturiki Passage, Wakaya, Gau, and the southern Lau islands are some of the best reef sites in Fiji.

Beqa is the most easily reached. It is an undersea plateau that is several miles wide. Clusters of coral pinnacles from 29.5–69 feet (9–21 m) high are scattered over the plateau on which two islands break the surface of the sea.

Plantation Island and surrounding coral reef, Fiji

At the turning of the tide, clumps of soft coral regain their beauty. As the water swishes over the coral, pinnacles of pink, lavender, red, or yellow are soon alive with bright fish feeding on the plankton brought in by the moving waters.

At Astrolabe Reef, part of the reef is created by masses of brilliantly colored soft corals and sponges. Another part of the reef has a purple soft coral growing so well that it covers a whole section of the reef.

Rainbow Reef has a vertical reef line and strong currents that carry an abundant supply of food to the reef dwellers.

One island in the Laus has a huge chasm slicing through its reef, 131 feet (40 m) below the surface. Near this huge stony arch, tomato clownfish dart among clusters of enormous sea anemones.

Papua New Guinea

The reefs of the scattered outer islands of Papua New Guinea are remote, clean, and untouched. This is a place of great variety where many unusual species of marine life flourish. The creatures that live there are rare, beautiful, vivid, and strangely shaped. For example, this is the home of the rare chambered nautilus that only lives at depths of 1,000 feet (305 m) or more.

A shallow reef running out from a little fishing village at Cape Vogel is the unlikely resting place of a B-17 Blackjack Bomber. Lost in a storm and out of fuel, the crew emergency landed onto the shallow reef. Mostly unhurt, they climbed onto the plane's wing, then jumped into the shallow water and made their way ashore. The bomber then sank and is now one of the diving spots of a lifetime.

The Maldive Islands

Situated in the Indian Ocean, the Maldives consist of about 1,196 atolls. So many are below the surface that it is not safe for boats to travel at night. By day, in bright sunlight, sparkling reefs stretch as far as the eye can see. The shallow reefs and friendly fish make this a paradise for divers. Coral gardens slope to deep ledges where thousands of brightly colored butterfly fish, angelfish, and triggerfish drift on the currents. Underneath the shadowy ledges away from the sunlight, squirrelfish and soldierfish inhabit their darkened world.

The Maldive Islands lose more and more land to the sea each year.

Thailand

The Simian Islands north of Phuket offer two completely different reefs. On their western side the reefs are made up of massive boulders linked together by small soft coral colonies. Powerful currents sweep through the reefs making fish dart quickly from boulder to boulder to find shelter.

The eastern side, in contrast, is sheltered, with gently sloping coral gardens. Soft and branching corals have colonized this area, which is richly populated by tropical fish.

The Galapagos Islands

Swift currents and murky waters mark the Galapagos Islands. There are no pretty coral reefs here, only boulder-strewn undersea mountains formed by volcanic activity. Rising steeply from the ocean floor, the Galapagos Islands are unique. From deep within the Earth, a thermal plume rises, building volcanoes underneath the tectonic plate. The Nazca Plate, on which the Galapagos Islands ride, drifts very slowly, only about an inch each year, in a southeastern direction.

The islands are distant from any other land mass and therefore are like no other place on the Earth. They belong to Ecuador, which lies 584 miles (940 km) to the west. The vegetation, animals, and climate are particular only to the Galapagos Islands.

Diver exploring the depths

There can be found both marine and land iguana, fur seals, the giant tortoise, and a huge variety of birdlife. Schools of hammerhead sharks, sailfish, manta rays, and even the occasional whale shark cruise through the watery darkness. At a depth of 98 feet (30 m), the water suddenly becomes clear and the temperature drops.

Palau

The Blue Corner on the island of Palau in the Pacific Ocean is a coral corner in a towering coral wall that is swept by powerful currents. On its deeper slopes, coral colonies blossom in pink, purple, and yellow. Brilliant pink gorgonians wave in the moving water. In the blue waters above, sharks patrol in company with schools of barracuda.

The Blue Hole, which is farther south on the reef, is an undersea cavern 108 feet (33 m) below the ocean's surface. It is accessed by four vertical tunnels through the reef. Divers can swim beneath the reef wall then return to the surface up the face of the coral precipice.

Brilliant pink gorgonians wave in the moving water.

Yap

The sun-drenched lagoon on the island of Yap in the Pacific Ocean has a plentiful supply of plankton, which brings the graceful manta rays to feed. A large coral shelf at the north end of the island creates a natural feeding place where divers can swim with as many as six of these huge, graceful creatures.

The Philippines

The Philippines consist of 7,000 islands. Over the years, overfishing has killed off some of the most famous reefs surrounding some of these islands. The extinction or huge reduction in numbers of one species affects others dramatically in this delicate ecosystem. Where once there was a huge variety of marine life with colorful shallows, sheer vertical walls, and gardens of soft coral, now there is devastation. New reefs may be found in deeper waters, in time. Until then, we must wait for nature to repair the damage caused by people.

Safari POWER

Choose a, b, or c?

Word Meanings

abrasions
a — *sea creatures*
b — *arguments*
c — *scrapes*

ferocious
a — *docile*
b — *savage*
c — *tiny*

pinnacles
a — *underwater gear*
b — *base areas*
c — *peaks*

plateau
a — *flat land surface*
b — *rugged mountain*
c — *cliff*

sanctuary
a — *danger*
b — *safe place*
c — *cleanliness*

skeletal
a — *huge*
b — *tidy*
c — *of a skeleton*

tantalize
a — *offend*
b — *dissuade*
c — *tempt*

tumultuous
a — *wild*
b — *tranquil*
c — *solid*

turbulent
a — *thick*
b — *calm*
c — *rough*

unimaginable
a — *hard to imagine*
b — *invisible*
c — *easy to imagine*

unique
a — *usual*
b — *like nothing else*
c — *unoriginal*

voracious
a — *greedily hungry*
b — *excitable*
c — *feeble*

Answers on page 21

Breakfast

Written by Zac Sutton

Algae was out for a morning swim,
Coral Polyp was studying him.
"Breakfast!" said Coral and gobbled him down.

Crown-of-Thorns Starfish was having great fun,
Out on the coral reef, blocking the sun.
"Breakfast!" it said and sucked Coral inside.

Seal was out for a morning swim,
Crown-of-Thorns Starfish was hiding from him.
"Breakfast!" said Seal, crunching him down.

Killer Whale was out on a cruise,
Spotting Seal, there was no time to lose.
"Breakfast!" he said, with a gleam in his eye.

MYSTERY of the Coral Reef

Written by Sally Cole • Illustrated by Anton Petrov

Jack squinted as the spray from the waves stung his eyes. Beneath his feet the deck shook as the boat was lifted on yet another wave. Up and up went the boat – onto the crest of a wave, then the world fell away, as it crashed with almost timber-shattering force down into the trough of water. Then the agonizing process began all over again.

"How can this be happening?" Jack thought, shaking his head in disbelief at the dilemma they were in.

Jack and his parents were part way through their trip around the world when disaster had struck. Because they'd left their last destination in a hurry, Jack's father had failed to notify anyone of their destination.

Jack knew that this meant nobody would come looking for them if they ended up shipwrecked on the coral reef that lay directly in the boat's path. They would be left to fend for themselves, if in fact they even survived.

Each time the boat corkscrewed at the top of a wave, the reef drew very ominously closer.

Jack's knuckles shone white through the skin of his hands as he clenched his fingers on the wheel. Bracing himself against the ferocious storm, he struggled to turn the boat away from what seemed like certain disaster.

Bracing himself against the ferocious storm, he struggled to turn the boat away from what seemed like certain disaster.

In the cabin below, tied to the bunk so he wouldn't be thrown around in the storm, lay the body of Jack's father, who had been killed when the boat's mast had crashed onto the deck when the storm first struck.

Together, Jack and his mother had chopped through the tangle of rigging to free his father from the debris.

They had hoped to ride out the storm, but deep down they both knew they were going to be blown onto the reef.

Another wave crashed over the bow of the ship where Jack was still fighting valiantly for control of the boat. Once again, the wheel was ripped out of his hands as the rudder below the waves took on a life of its own and steered the ship back into danger. He blinked the salt water out of his eyes and tried to concentrate again – getting ready for the next onslaught of water – and still the reef got closer.

He glanced over at his mother, who was staring into space. She hadn't been the same since the mast had killed his father. It was only hours ago, but it seemed like a lifetime. All Jack could think of was trying to get them out of this awful mess.

In her hands, Jack's mother was holding a leather bag containing her wedding ring, her jewels, and a small fortune in money.

"Jack," she said, "if the boat sinks, you will have a good chance of surviving. You must take our money and my jewels. They'll help you to start a new life."

"No!" Jack had cried "You keep them. We're both going to make it."

Jack's mother smiled and hugged him tight. "If not, you must be very strong," she said, tying the bag firmly around her son's waist.

Jack blinked back tears at the thought. Losing one parent was unbearable, but losing two would be a tragedy. He was glad the spray from the waves hid his tears. He knew he needed to be strong for his mother.

Just then, he happened to glance over his shoulder in time to see a mountain of water, roaring in as fast as a train, engulf the boat.

The wave picked the boat up like a toy, flung it high, then threw it onto the reef. The boat landed with a mighty thud, shattering its hull. Wood, rope, and canvas flew everywhere.

Luckily for Jack, he had been slammed into a wall of the cabin. He hit the wall with such force, it collapsed, but as it did so, it broke his fall, which meant he missed smashing himself on the reef. He sighed with relief.

However, before he had time to recover, another wave swept over the reef, throwing him off the wall and onto the coral. The pain was instant and sharp as he landed on the coral.

"Mother!" he screamed, wanting to hear a reassuring voice and to know where she was. But he couldn't move because he was in too much agony from the sharp shards of coral that seemed to pierce every part of his body.

He then lost consciousness because the trauma was too much for his mind to handle.

When he came to, Jack was face down on the reef, with parts of the sharp marine life digging into his face. His sore feet were being lapped by the now gentle waves.

Blood oozed from coral grazes and cuts and stained the water pink. He could see that the coral formed the outer part of a lagoon. On the other side of the lagoon was the sanctuary of a beach and a foreshore with lush green grass and trees behind. The water in the lagoon was now calm and the sun shone harshly on his exposed skin.

Jack hurt everywhere. Slowly he rose to his knees. Staggering and falling he jumped into the water and slowly swam the short distance to the beach.

When he reached land he fell onto the sand, which felt like a soft pillow compared to the coral reef. He lay still for a moment, oblivious to the stinging sensation of the sand in his cuts and abrasions, then his eyes closed as he fell again into unconsciousness – his last thoughts being of his mother and father.

His head throbbed from a huge lump on his forehead.

Unbeknown to him, the leather bag had dropped from his waist as he swam across the lagoon. The incoming tide had deposited it behind a boulder at the side of a small cave.

Hours later, Jack awoke. His head throbbed from a huge lump on his forehead. He tottered along the beach and collapsed on the sand again.

Jack put his head in his hands and wept – thinking of his parents. He was feeling light-headed when he heard some voices behind him. Then he fell into a dream-filled sleep. He dreamed of voices and hands touching him. He opened his eyes – three pairs of eyes gazed down at him. He blinked. The voices he was hearing were real.

"How did you get here?" said one of the voices. "Did you come from the storm?"

Jack tried to remember. He remembered the beach. But that was all! Nothing else.

"I... I don't know, I can't remember. I can't remember anything," Jack said, feeling panic rising inside him.

"I'm Bill Bradley and these are my children, Cathy and Josh," said one of the voices. "You must have gotten a huge whack on the head. That can make your memory a bit fuzzy, but it'll come back in time. Try not to worry. We'll take you home with us and fix those nasty cuts. You'll feel better with dry clothes and some hot food inside you."

The three made a cradle of their hands and carried Jack up the beach, and up the grassy slope. After a fairly short walk, they arrived at a house. Finally, Jack felt safe.

It took weeks for Jack to recover, but still he couldn't remember anything. Bill and a few of his friends checked around the beach, but other than a couple of planks, nothing remained of the boat. It was a mystery to them.

Bill regularly checked all the local newspapers and police departments, but he never found a report of any missing persons in any of the reports.

Even though Jack stayed with the Bradley family and they treated him like a son, the question remained in the back of his mind – who was he and where did he come from?

Because he didn't know his name, the Bradleys decided to call him John. He agreed with the name. There was something both familiar and unfamiliar about it.

Over the next few years John, Cathy, and Josh spent most of their summers in the water and on the sands of the beach. They swam, sailed boats, paddled canoes, and built bonfires.

Occasionally the rest of the Bradleys would spot John sitting alone on a sand dune looking over at the coral reef. Not once was he ever tempted to swim out there and look for any clues to his identity. He didn't know why, but in the back of his mind he knew something bad had happened there.

One day, several years after the shipwreck, John and Cathy were walking along the beach when something glinted in the sun, catching Cathy's eye.

"What's that?" said Cathy.

"What's what?" replied John.

"Over by the cave, I thought I saw something glittering in the sun."

"I didn't see anything," said John, "but let's go and take a look."

"Over by the cave, I thought I saw something glittering in the sun."

As they approached the mouth of the cave, the sun caught the object again.

"See?" said Cathy excitedly, as she ran up to the boulder next to the cave.

"I saw it that time," said John, who was following close behind.

Cathy knelt down and picked up what looked like a rotting piece of leather. As she stood up again the leather fell apart in her hands, and a plethora of jewels, gems, and coins fell to the ground.

Her own gasp of astonishment was overshadowed by a deep sound of anguish coming from John. As she turned to look at him she didn't know what shocked her most – the treasure spread on the sand by her feet or the look of pain on his face.

She put her hand on his shoulder. "What's the matter, John?" she said.

"It's Jack," he replied.

"Sorry?" said Cathy.

"It's coming back to me, Cathy. My real name's Jack," he said quietly.

"Oh, my goodness," said Cathy, a little bewildered. She wasn't sure if he was telling her the truth or not. "How can you be sure?"

He knelt in the sand and picked up some of the jewels. Something flickered in his memory. He had a faraway look in his eyes as he spoke.

"These belonged to my mother," he started slowly, his memory flooding back to him even as he spoke. "I remember her giving them to me just before our boat hit the coral reef. I also remember my father being killed by our mast falling. I think it was when the storm first struck."

"You must be right," said Cathy. "I remember there was a storm the day we found you on the beach, John... Jack."

He nodded, a few tears starting to fall down his cheeks. Jack looked at the gems and coins and started gathering them absent-mindedly.

Cathy gave him a hug. "Well, I guess that's one mystery solved," she said enthusiastically.

Jack nodded in agreement. "I guess it is," he replied, sadly.

Safari POINT OF VIEW

Fax: Page 1 of 2

What's the Big Problem?

I don't understand why people are so opposed to the natural resources around the Great Barrier Reef being uncovered and used. If it's there, we should use it. A whole lot of oil has to be far more useful to humankind than a reef just sitting in the ocean. The demand for oil in the world can only increase. I'm sure there are ways of getting at it that aren't too destructive, anyway, if that's what people are worrying about.

Fax: Page 2 of 2

Similarly, I believe that there is nothing wrong with coral harvesting. If it's there, and useful, we should make use of it, surely. Coral is just skeletal waste, isn't it?

I don't understand it myself, but some people think it makes a wonderful garden or home ornament. Why shouldn't they be able to collect the pieces they want? It makes much more sense than having the stuff sitting uselessly underwater.

New Reply Reply All Forward Delete Send & Receive

- **Inbox**
- **Outbox**
- **Sent Mail**
- **Deleted**
- **Drafts**
- **Contacts**

Subject: Don't Blame the Divers

I've been a diver for over 15 years now and I like to think I have a lot of respect for the underwater world. Lately I've been reading how some people think divers can inadvertently damage reef structures. I disagree. I am extremely careful when diving. I never touch any coral and certainly never stand on it or break any part off.

I suppose it's feasible that some divers are more careless than me, but generally the people I've met who are interested in diving are thoughtful and respectful.

Safari POWER

Answers

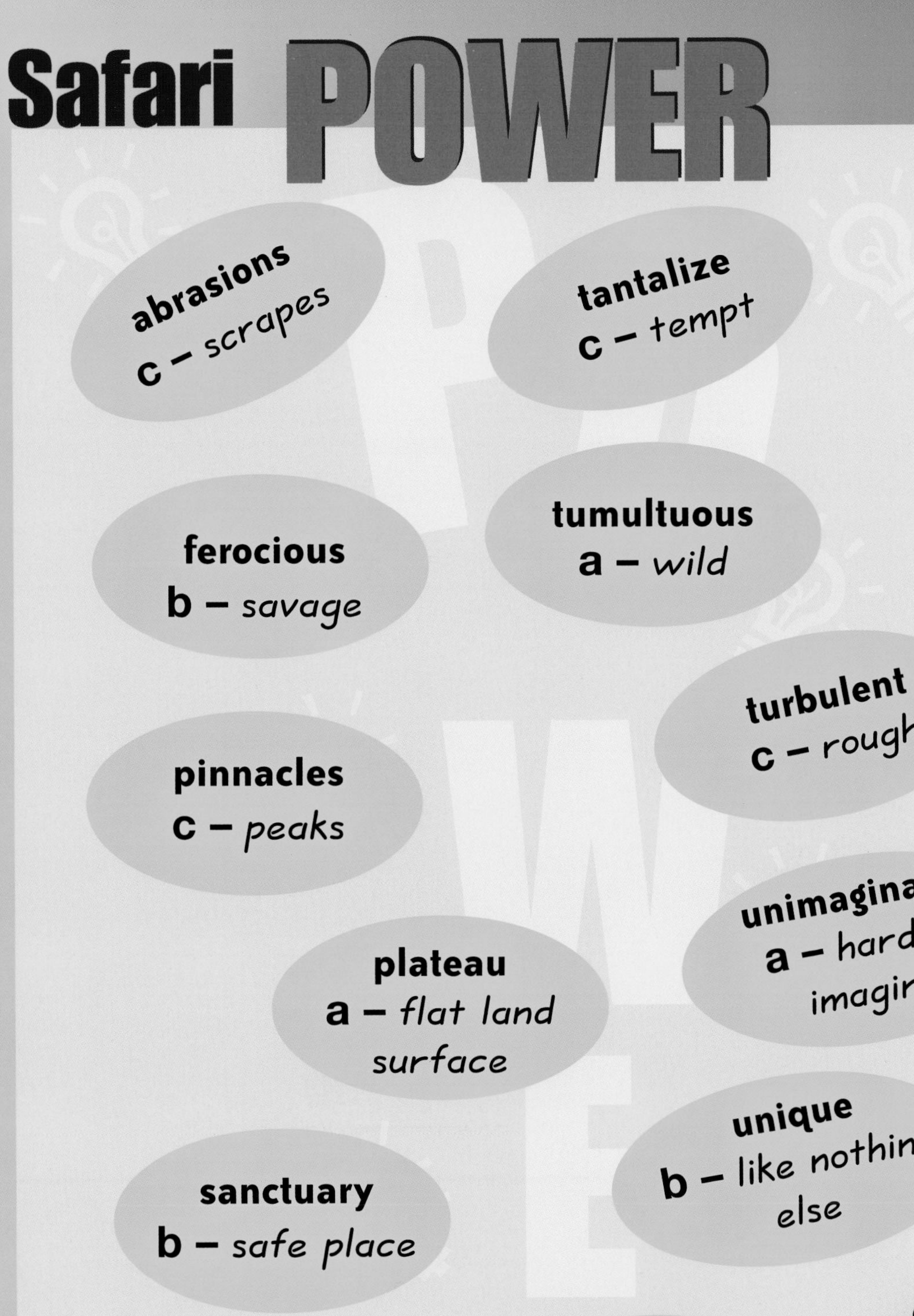

abrasions
c – *scrapes*

tantalize
c – *tempt*

ferocious
b – *savage*

tumultuous
a – *wild*

turbulent
c – *rough*

pinnacles
c – *peaks*

unimaginable
a – *hard to imagine*

plateau
a – *flat land surface*

unique
b – *like nothing else*

sanctuary
b – *safe place*

skeletal
c – *of a skeleton*

voracious
a – *greedily hungry*

Rating Scale

10-12 Excellent | 7-9 Very good | 4-6 Good | 0-3 Try again

Xtra for Xperts

What does flourish mean?

Treasure

Written by Brianna Osborne

Characters

Amos

Dad

Emerald

Narrator

Nathan

Setting

On a beach after a wild storm

Scene 1

Narrator
For days a storm had lashed the beach. Huge breakers crashed over the reef. The waves swept over the sand. They swept away boulders and sand that had built up over the years. They reopened a little cave that had remained hidden at the far end of the beach. Emerald, Nathan, and Amos are playing near the beach.

Emerald
Come on, you guys. The weather's settled down. Let's explore! The beach looks so different after the storm.

Amos
It sure does. Bet I can beat you to the bottom.

Narrator
Grabbing his cardboard box, Amos starts sliding down the grassy slope.

Emerald
I'm just going to walk.

Narrator
Emerald picks her way carefully down the slope. She walks along the beach, occasionally stopping to pick up a shell or an interesting piece of coral from the sand.

Emerald
There's so much coral on the beach after the storm. It's sharp, too.

Nathan
Looks like half the reef has blown onto the beach! I hope the reef hasn't been damaged too much.

Narrator
When Emerald reaches the end of the beach, she stops suddenly.

Emerald
Hey! There's a cool cave here! I don't remember seeing it before.

Nathan
It must have been hidden by all that grass and sand.

Narrator
Amos arrives. He's been caught up in a thorny bush and is still picking prickles out of his hands.

Amos *(out of breath)*
Wow. A cave. You'd think we'd have seen it before. We've been here so many times.

Nathan
I think the storm must have uncovered it!

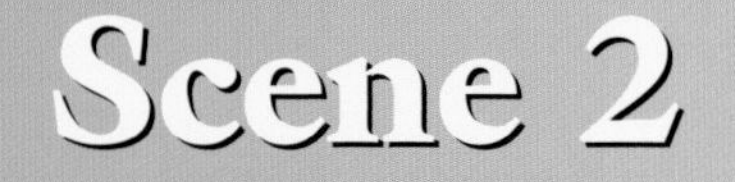

Emerald
I'm going in. I'm a bit smaller than you two. I'll squeeze around behind that boulder.

Amos
Is that a good idea? You don't know what you might find.

Nathan
Maybe he's right, Emerald. Maybe we should get Dad. It could be dangerous.

Emerald
How? Anyway, there's no way I'm waiting for Dad. That'd take too long. I'm going in right now, otherwise I'll never know. So, here goes.

Narrator
Emerald forces her way into the small gap in the entranceway to the cave, which is all that has been uncovered by the storm. The others wait outside. They've forgotten their apprehension and are very curious.

Nathan
What's it like in there?

Amos
Can you see anything?

Emerald
It's dark! And stuffy.

Nathan
You're doing well. You're nearly in.

Emerald
Hold on! There's something wedged behind this boulder.

Narrator
Emerald heaves and pulls.

Emerald
I can't shift it. It feels like leather, maybe a bag of some sort, but it's stuck tight.

Narrator
Nathan and Amos can't wait to find out what's beside the boulder.

Nathan
You come out, Em. Let me try.

Amos
Hurry!

Emerald
OK. I'll have to back out, though. There's not enough room for me to turn around.

Narrator
Emerald emerges, brushing bits of dry grass and sand from her hair. Nathan forces his way into the small space.

Nathan
I think I'm stuck!

Amos
Wriggle a bit. You should be able to squeeze through.

Emerald
Can you see the bag?

Nathan
No. I can't see anything. It's too dark. It doesn't smell too good in here, either. You didn't mention that!

Emerald
Just feel around beside that big boulder on your left.

Nathan
You're right. There is something. I can just reach it.

Narrator
Grunting noises come from within the cave.

Emerald
He's taking his time.

Nathan
Got it!

Narrator
Nathan backs carefully, and with some difficulty, from the cave, holding a stained leather bag in his hands. The three children kneel on the sand.

Nathan
There's definitely something inside. It's pretty bulky.

Emerald
Open it! Quick!

Amos
Let me help!

Nathan
The bag is hard. The sea has made the leather dry out. It's all stiff.

Amos
I've got my pocketknife! Here, let me cut the ties.

Narrator
Amos slides the knife blade under the leather ties and saws through them.

Nathan
That's it. Great! If I shake it a bit – there. Oh!

Emerald
Wow!

Amos
It looks like green fire! It's a necklace!

Emerald
Look at all the gold and silver coins, and that looks like a wedding ring! There are so many other jewels, too. I've never seen anything like it! This is amazing.

Narrator
The children stare at each other incredulously.

Amos
I wonder how long it's been in the cave for?

Nathan
From the state of that bag, I'd say quite a long time.

Amos
It does seem pretty ancient.

Emerald
Let's go and show Dad. Help me put everything back in the bag.

Narrator
They carefully place the treasure back in the bag, making sure they get every last coin. Then they run home.

Scene 3

Narrator
The three children burst into the house, slamming the door behind them.

Emerald *(gasping for breath)*
Dad!

Amos
Look what we found!

Nathan
In a cave on the beach!

Narrator
Nathan holds the bag out. His father leans over, peers at the bag, then reaches for a chair and collapses into it.

Emerald
Are you all right, Dad? You look as if you've seen a ghost!

Dad
Where did you find this?

Amos
In a cave on the beach.

Dad
What cave? I've never seen a cave down there.

Nathan
The storm must have opened up the entrance. It must have been a secret for years and years.

Dad
I can't believe it. I just can't believe it.

Narrator
Emerald sits beside her father.

Dad
It looks like you children may have found some treasure from a ship that was wrecked on the reef many years ago.

Amos
How do you know, Dad?

Dad
It was in all the papers at the time. A ship was wrecked during a massive storm, much like the one we've just had. A family was onboard who was moving over here.

Nathan
Were there any survivors?

Dad
There was only one, a little girl. She was found on the reef by a local fisherman. She was quite badly injured and, of course, very shocked by the deaths of her whole family. But the fisherman looked after her for a while and then eventually, when she was well enough, she went back home to England to live with some of her relatives.

Emerald
The poor thing.

Nathan
What about the boat?

Dad
There was hardly any wreckage. The boat was so badly damaged that there was next to nothing washed ashore.

Emerald
How do you know that the treasure comes from that ship, Dad?

Amos
Yeah, it might have been in that cave for hundreds of years. It might even be pirate treasure!

Dad
Well, the little girl said her parents had put all their money and jewels into a leather bag for safe keeping during the storm. Her grandmother had died shortly before the family set out, leaving everything to her daughter, the little girl's mother. That's why there were so many jewels.

Nathan
Did anyone look for it?

Dad
You bet they did. But it was never seen again. People began to think maybe the little girl had been making the whole thing up, or had gotten confused.

Emerald
It's so sad.

Amos
It sure is.

Nathan
Did you ever look for the treasure, Dad?

Dad
Yes, your uncles and I spent many summers hunting for the treasure up and down the beach, but we never found anything but fishing nets and coral.

Narrator
Dad then picks up the stained leather bag. He tips the contents onto the kitchen table. The coins, jewels, and sparkling emeralds glow. They all stare at the unimaginable treasure.

Emerald
Dad, do you think that little girl is still alive? We should try to find her, shouldn't we?

Dad
My thoughts exactly, Emerald. I'll be making a call to the police tomorrow morning.

Nathan
But we found the treasure. Shouldn't we be able to keep it?

Amos
Yeah. What's the point of finding treasure if you don't get to keep it?

Dad
I'm sorry, boys. I know you'd like to keep the treasure. We all would. But think how much it would mean to its owner to have it returned after all this time. It doesn't belong to us.

Nathan
I guess.

Amos *(resigned)*
You're right, Dad. We should return it.

Narrator
Dad puts an arm around each boy, glad they understand that the treasure isn't theirs to keep.

Coral Canyons

Written by Amanda Brownfeather

Coral canyons call to me,
From deep beneath the tumultuous sea,
Here may I drift at one with the waves,
Exploring mystical, marvelous caves.

Coral canyons, my special place,
Beautiful fish in every space,
Darting and drifting through forests of weed,
Moving wherever the currents may lead.

Coral canyons, the shades of a dream,
Through sunshine shafts, pearly shells gleam,
Treasure to watch, to let live its life,
Undisturbed, free from the diver's cruel knife.

Coral canyons tantalize me,
Tempting, teasing, beckoning me,
Reefs that glow with hues of fire,
Herein lies my heart's desire.

readingsafari.com
Check out these Safari magazines, too!
Reading SAFARI Magazine
Gold Fever
SAFARI Magazine
KOMODO DRAGONS AND OTHER LARGE LIZARDS
Have your say -
e-mail your Safari Tour Guide at
tourguide@readingsafari.com
New
Reply
Reply All
Forward
Delete
Send & Receive
• Inbox
• Outbox
• Sent Mail
• Deleted
• Drafts
Subject: Coral and Other Reefs
Now you have read this magazine, is there anything you feel strongly about? E-mail your point of view to the Safari Tour Guide.
Find some fun things to do!
Go to –
http://www.readingsafari.com
Safari Superstar
Name – Emerald Stravous
Age – 12
Find out more about this Safari Superstar at
http://www.readingsafari.com